Associated Board Brass Scales and Arpeggios

Series Editors **John Wallace** and **Ian Denley**

£2.99
C20

Scales and Arpeggios for Tuba 𝄢 (in Bb, C, Eb and F)

Grades 1-8

It is often maintained, with some justification, that brass-players frequently show reluctance to learn scales and arpeggios thoroughly. But as they form the basis of a fluent technique and help to stabilize range and accuracy, a methodical and thorough preparation of scales and arpeggios is essential.

This manual seeks to assist this situation by including a comprehensive fingering chart for the four 𝄢 tubas which feature here, together with hints on problems to avoid and useful advice appended to the scales and arpeggios most likely to be problematic. The aim is to help students learn their scales and arpeggios thoroughly, as well as provide support material for those brass teachers who may not be specialists on this group of instruments.

We are most grateful to Patrick Harrild, Principal Tuba with the London Symphony Orchestra and Professor at the Royal Academy of Music and the Guildhall School of Music, and Bob Childs, Head of Brass at Hymers College, Hull, and Principal Euphonium of the Black Dyke Mills Brass Band, for acting as specialist advisers to this manual.

JOHN WALLACE and IAN DENLEY   1995

The Associated Board of the Royal Schools of Music

Fingering chart

This composite fingering chart covers all four of the tubas dealt with in this manual. It gives fingerings for the range of notes covered by the Associated Board's examinations, although the instrument can reach a great many notes outside its basic compass. It also gives a number of alternative fingerings. Although there exists a wide variety of instruments called tuba with numbers of valves ranging from 3 to 7, this manual accommodates the basic three-valve instrument and gives alternative fingerings featuring the more usual 4th valve. Instruments which have a 4th valve may draw upon the additional shaded fingerings.

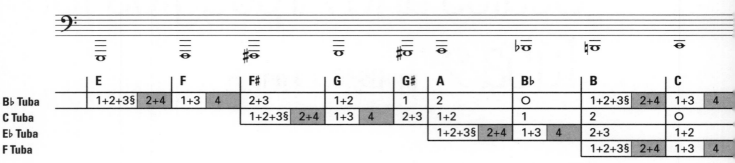

	E	F	F#	G	G#	A	B♭	B	C
B♭ Tuba	1+2+3§ / 2+4	1+3 / 4	2+3	1+2	1	2	O	1+2+3§ / 2+4	1+3 / 4
C Tuba			1+2+3§ / 2+4	1+3 / 4	2+3	1+2	1	2	O
E♭ Tuba						1+2+3§ / 2+4	1+3 / 4	2+3	1+2
F Tuba								1+2+3§ / 2+4	1+3 / 4

	C#	D	E♭	E	F	F#	G	G#	A	B♭
B♭ Tuba	2+3	1+2	1	2	O	2+3	1+2 / 3	1	2	O
C Tuba	1+2+3§ / 2+4	1+3 / 4	2+3	1+2	1	2	O	2+3	1+2 / 3	1
E♭ Tuba	1	2	O	1+2+3§ / 2+4	1+3 / 4	2+3	1+2 / 3	1	2	O
F Tuba	2+3	1+2	1	2	O	1+2+3§ / 2+4	1+3 / 4	2+3	1+2 / 3	1

	B	C	C#	D	E♭	E	F	F#	G	G#
B♭ Tuba	1+2 / 3	1	2	O	1	2	O	2+3	1+2 / 3	1
C Tuba	2	O	1+2 / 3	1	2	O	1	2	O	1
E♭ Tuba	2+3	1+2 / 3	1	2	O	1+2 / 3	1	2	O	1
F Tuba	2	O	2+3	1+2 / 3	1	2	O	1+2	1	2

	A	B♭	B	C	C#	D	E♭	E	F
B♭ Tuba	2	O							
C Tuba	1+2 / 3	1	2	O					
E♭ Tuba	2	O	2+3	1+2	1	2	O		
F Tuba	O	1	2	O	2+3	1+2	1	2	O

Key to symbols

1	press index finger	3	press ring finger
2	press middle finger	O	all fingers off
		4	press 4th valve
		§	on tubas without compensating tubing this note is sharp and will need embouchure adjustment.

Tables of harmonics

As a source for the exploration of alternative fingerings, the following tables illustrate the notes available from each combination of the basic three valves (i.e. each length of tubing). This is known as the *harmonic series*. The first note in the harmonic series is known as the *fundamental* or *pedal note*, but the only practicable one on the tuba is available from the open fingering (O). The numbered notes which follow the fundamental, obtainable from each valve combination by embouchure adjustment, are known as *harmonics*, or *upper partials*.

Although the tuba is most commonly used in its lowest register, very high notes within its range occasionally feature in some of the more complex repertoire. Strictly speaking, there is no upper limit to the harmonic series, but it must be stressed that these extremes of range should only be undertaken by the highly advanced player.

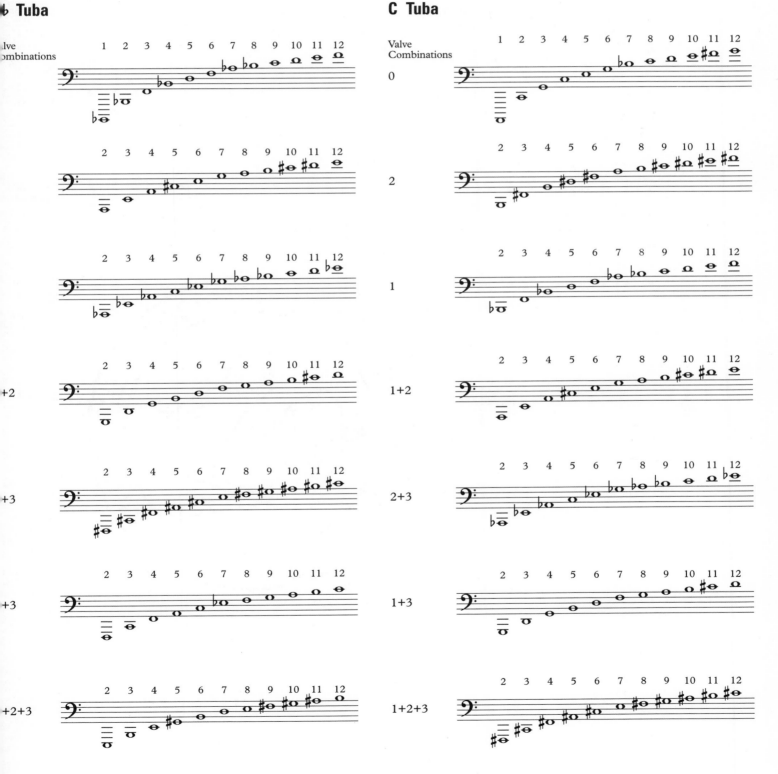

Eb Tuba

Valve Combinations

F Tuba

Valve Combinations

Guide to fingering

For reference purposes, where notes are indicated throughout the manual with a small superscript number (e.g. Bb^1, E^2, $F\#^3$, etc.), this refers to their position within the tuba's range:

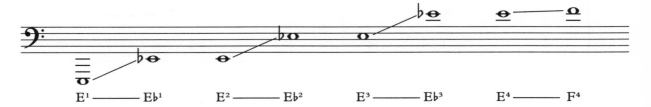

The range of notes for each tuba within the Associated Board's scales and arpeggios is as follows:

Bb Tuba: E^1-Bb^3 C Tuba: $F\#^1$-C^3
Eb Tuba: A^1-Eb^3 F Tuba: B^1-F^4

Posture, fingering and grip

The importance of developing a good posture (frequently overlooked by brass players) is essential in the process of natural breathing, which is vital in the study of scales and arpeggios. The parts of the body involved must be kept comfortably in balance, whether standing or sitting.

For really fluent scales and arpeggios the hand depressing the valves must be relaxed. Most of the weight bearing of the instrument should be taken by the other hand. A sideways pressure when depressing the valve should be avoided as it will impair the valve action.

The 4th valve

The 4th valve is the most common additional valve found on the tuba. It provides an excellent opportunity for options in tuning, as well as facility in fingering, and if available should always be used.

Maintenance

It is important that all valves and tuning slides be kept lubricated for optimum performance.

Intonation

Intonation and the careful negotiation of intervals should feature greatly in the study of scales and arpeggios. They are affected by many factors: the size of the oral cavity, the position of the tongue and the quality of sound (quality of sound profoundly affects pitch).

Generally, the best fingering to use is the one that is in tune. Some experimentation is usually necessary, especially at the top of the range where the harmonics are closer together.

The lowest notes of each tuba's range, fingered 1+2+3 and 1+3, are usually sharp. Tuba players can compensate by using the alternative fingerings involving the 4th valve where this is available. In the unlikely event of the 4th valve being unavailable, the player can learn to temper the intonation with the embouchure through careful listening.

Enharmonic note-names

Two or three notes having the same sound but different names are called *enharmonics*; for example, Eb is the enharmonic of D#. A full table is given below to guide students in the fingering of those notes in certain scales and arpeggios which may be unfamiliarly notated.

C	=	B#	=	Dbb		E	=	Fb	=	Dx		G#	=	Ab		
C#	=	Db	=	Bx		F	=	E#	=	Gbb		A	=	Gx	=	Bbb
D	=	Cx	=	Ebb		F#	=	Gb	=	Ex		Bb	=	A#	=	Cbb
Eb	=	D#	=	Fbb		G	=	Fx	=	Abb		B	=	Cb	=	Ax

Notes on the requirements

Reference must always be made to the syllabus for the year in which the examination is to be taken, in case any changes have been made to the requirements.

In the examination all scales and arpeggios must be played from memory.

Candidates should aim to play their scales and arpeggios at a pace that allows accuracy, with a uniform tone across all registers and a rhythmic flow without undue accentuation, as well as with even tonguing and good intonation. Recommended speeds are given on page 9.

In Grades 1-5 candidates may choose *either* the melodic *or* the harmonic form of the minor scale; in Grades 6-8 candidates are required to play *both* forms.

The choice of breathing place is left to the candidate's discretion, but taking a breath must not be allowed to disturb the flow of the scale or arpeggio. If a breath is taken during the course of a slurred scale or arpeggio, a soft tongue attack should be made on the note following the breath.

Given the enormous amount of breath required by the tuba, especially in its lowest range, students should aim for the best musical result by keeping the unavoidably frequent breaths as unostentatious as possible.

Articulation

It is very important for the foundation of good articulation that players use the *tongue* to articulate, rather than just the breath, which is a common error at the elementary level. The sound must be well-supported by diaphragmatic breathing throughout all forms of articulation, so that the tone does not deteriorate, (usually with attendant intonation problems), especially when tonguing *staccato*.

Four different forms of articulation are found in the scale and arpeggio requirements: slurred, tongued, *legato*-tongued and *staccato*. In Grades 1-6 candidates are required to play scales and arpeggios both slurred and tongued; in Grades 7 and 8 candidates are required to play scales and arpeggios slurred, *legato*-tongued and *staccato*.

In slurred scales and arpeggios there is no gap between the notes, whereas the gap is large when playing *staccato*. In *legato*-tonguing the effect is almost slurred, but there is the smallest separation achieved by a very soft tongue attack.

The articulations may be visualized like this:

slurred	_____
tongued	___ ___ ___ ___
legato-tongued	_____ _____ _____ _____
staccato	_ _ _ _

Legato-tonguing is often considered by brass players to be a fusion of *tenuto* and *legato*; it is sometimes described as 'soft'-tonguing or as an articulated slur. Perhaps the least familiar of the articulation forms required, it may usefully be notated as follows:

Current requirements for Grades 1-8

These tables list scales and arpeggios required for each grade; numbers refer to those printed alongside the scales and arpeggios in the following pages.

B♭ Tuba

Grade 1   39, 89 *or* 90, 199, 227

Grade 2   1, 30, 45 *or* 46, 89 *or* 90, 161, 190, 205, 227

Grade 3   4, 7, 27, 55 *or* 56, 117 *or* 118, 149, 164, 167, 187, 210, 241

Grade 4   10, 23, 32, 61 *or* 62, 93 *or* 94, 111 *or* 112, 146, 170, 183, 192, 213, 229, 238

Grade 5   20, 24, 32, 43, 81 *or* 82, 101 *or* 102, 125 *or* 126, 150, 180, 184, 192, 203, 223, 233, 245, 259

Grade 6   2, 16, 28, 33, 85, 86, 95, 96, 103, 104, 121, 122, 139, 143, 144, 145, 162, 176, 188, 193, 225, 230, 234, 243, 247, 265

Grade 7   2, 5, 8, 11, 16, 20, 24, 28, 33, 37, 41, 43, 47, 48, 51, 52, 57, 58, 63, 64, 73, 74, 81, 82, 85, 86, 95, 96, 103, 104, 113, 114, 121, 122, 125, 126, 139, 143, 144, 145, 147, 148, 162, 165, 168, 171, 176, 180, 184, 188, 193, 197, 201, 203, 206, 208, 211, 214, 219, 223, 225, 230, 234, 239, 243, 245, 248, 259, 260, 266, 267

Grade 8   2, 5, 8, 11, 16, 20, 24, 28, 33, 37, 42, 43, 47, 48, 51, 52, 57, 58, 63, 64, 73, 74, 81, 82, 85, 86, 95, 96, 103, 104, 113, 114, 123, 124, 125, 126, 139, 143, 144, 145, 147, 148, 151, 158, 159, 162, 165, 168, 171, 176, 180, 184, 188, 193, 197, 202, 203, 206, 208, 211, 214, 219, 223, 225, 230, 234, 239, 244, 245, 247, 248, 249, 250, 257, 259, 260, 266, 267, 268

C Tuba

Grade 1   1, 107 *or* 108, 161, 236

Grade 2   7, 39, 55 *or* 56, 107 *or* 108, 167, 199, 210, 236

Grade 3   10, 13, 36, 45 *or* 46, 67 *or* 68, 129, 170, 173, 196, 205, 216

Grade 4   17, 32, 41, 75 *or* 76, 111 *or* 112, 125 *or* 126, 150, 177, 192, 201, 220, 238, 245

Grade 5   5, 28, 33, 41, 51 *or* 52, 95 *or* 96, 121 *or* 122, 130, 165, 188, 193, 201, 208, 230, 243, 247

Grade 6   8, 24, 37, 42, 47, 48, 103, 104, 113, 114, 123, 124, 144, 145, 147, 148, 168, 184, 197, 202, 206, 234, 239, 244, 249, 267

Grade 7   2, 5, 8, 11, 14, 18, 24, 28, 33, 37, 42, 44, 47, 48, 51, 52, 57, 58, 63, 64, 69, 70, 77, 78, 85, 86, 95, 96, 103, 104, 113, 114, 123, 124, 127, 128, 144, 145, 147, 148, 151, 152, 162, 165, 168, 171, 174, 178, 184, 188, 193, 197, 202, 204, 206, 208, 211, 214, 217, 221, 225, 230, 234, 239, 244, 246, 247, 248, 250, 268, 269

Grade 8   3, 5, 8, 11, 14, 18, 24, 28, 33, 37, 42, 44, 49, 50, 51, 52, 57, 58, 63, 64, 69, 70, 77, 78, 85, 86, 95, 96, 103, 104, 113, 114, 123, 124, 127, 128, 131, 144, 145, 147, 148, 151, 152, 153, 160, 163, 165, 168, 171, 174, 178, 184, 188, 193, 197, 202, 204, 207, 208, 211, 214, 217, 221, 225, 230, 234, 239, 244, 246, 247, 248, 249, 250, 251, 252, 260, 268, 269, 270

Eb Tuba

Grade 1   10, 45 *or* 46, 170, 205

Grade 2   4, 17, 45 *or* 46, 75 *or* 76, 164, 177, 205, 220

Grade 3   2, 21, 25, 61 *or* 62, 87 *or* 88, 135, 162, 181, 185, 213, 226

Grade 4   5, 29, 43, 47 *or* 48, 57 *or* 58, 97 *or* 98, 132, 165, 189, 203, 206, 211, 231

Grade 5   5, 14, 42, 44, 51 *or* 52, 69 *or* 70, 123 *or* 124, 136, 165, 174, 202, 204, 208, 217, 244, 250

Grade 6   3, 6, 18, 37, 49, 50, 53, 54, 63, 64, 127, 128, 131, 148, 151, 152, 163, 166, 178, 197, 207, 209, 214, 246, 252, 270

Grade 7   3, 6, 9, 11, 14, 18, 22, 26, 31, 37, 42, 44, 49, 50, 53, 54, 59, 60, 63, 64, 69, 70, 77, 78, 83, 84, 91, 92, 99, 100, 113, 114, 123, 124, 127, 128, 131, 133, 134, 148, 151, 152, 163, 166, 169, 171, 174, 178, 182, 186, 191, 197, 202, 204, 207, 209, 212, 214, 217, 221, 224, 228, 232, 239, 244, 246, 250, 251, 253, 261, 271

Grade 8   3, 6, 9, 12, 14, 18, 22, 26, 31, 37, 42, 44, 49, 50, 53, 54, 59, 60, 65, 66, 69, 70, 77, 78, 83, 84, 91, 92, 99, 100, 113, 114, 123, 124, 127, 128, 131, 133, 134, 137, 148, 151, 152, 154, 155, 163, 166, 169, 172, 174, 178, 182, 186, 191, 197, 202, 204, 207, 209, 212, 215, 217, 221, 224, 228, 232, 239, 244, 246, 249, 250, 251, 252, 253, 254, 255, 261, 262, 271

harmonic version.

F Tuba

Grade 1   17, 55 *or* 56, 177, 210

Grade 2   10, 25, 55 *or* 56, 87 *or* 88, 170, 185, 210, 226

Grade 3   8, 29, 34, 75 *or* 76, 105 *or* 106, 140, 168, 189, 194, 220, 235

Grade 4   5, 11, 38, 57 *or* 58, 69 *or* 70, 115 *or* 116, 136, 165, 171, 198, 211, 217, 240

Grade 5   3, 6, 11, 22, 49 *or* 50, 63 *or* 64, 83 *or* 84, 141, 163, 166, 171, 182, 207, 214, 224, 252

Grade 6   9, 12, 26, 44, 53, 54, 59, 60, 65, 66, 77, 78, 131, 133, 134, 152, 169, 172, 186, 204, 209, 212, 215, 221, 254, 261

Grade 7   3, 6, 9, 12, 15, 18, 22, 26, 31, 35, 40, 44, 49, 50, 53, 54, 59, 60, 65, 66, 71, 72, 77, 78, 83, 84, 91, 92, 99, 100, 109, 110, 119, 120, 127, 128, 131, 133, 134, 137, 138, 152, 163, 166, 169, 172, 175, 178, 182, 186, 191, 195, 200, 204, 207, 209, 212, 215, 218, 221, 224, 228, 232, 237, 242, 246, 252, 253, 255, 262, 263

Grade 8   3, 6, 9, 12, 15, 19, 22, 26, 31, 35, 40, 44, 49, 50, 53, 54, 59, 60, 65, 66, 71, 72, 79, 80, 83, 84, 91, 92, 99, 100, 109, 110, 119, 120, 127, 128, 131, 133, 134, 137, 138, 142, 152, 156, 157, 163, 166, 169, 172, 175, 179, 182, 186, 191, 195, 200, 204, 207, 209, 212, 215, 218, 222, 224, 228, 232, 237, 242, 246, 251, 252, 253, 254, 255, 256, 258, 262, 263, 264

Recommended speeds

The following recommended *minimum* speeds are given as a general guide. It is essential that scales and arpeggios are played at a speed rapid enough to allow well-organized breathing, yet steady enough to allow a well-focused sound with good intonation across the range.

major and minor scales, chromatic scales, whole-tone scales, dominant and diminished sevenths				*major and minor arpeggios*		
Grade 1	♩	=	50	♪	=	72
Grade 2	♩	=	56	♪	=	80
Grade 3	♩	=	66	♪	=	92
Grade 4	♩	=	72	♪	=	100
Grade 5	♩	=	80	♪	=	112
Grade 6	♩	=	104	♩.	=	56
Grade 7	♩	=	116	♩.	=	66
Grade 8	♩	=	132	♩.	=	76

Major Scales

C MAJOR 1 Octave

1 B♭ Tuba: keep the tone as full as possible as you ascend. Listen carefully to the intonation of both Cs, compensating with the 4th valve where available.
C Tuba: make sure that 3 goes down with 1 simultaneously on D. Listen carefully to the intonation on D, compensating with the 4th valve where available.

C MAJOR A Twelfth

2 B♭ Tuba: take care to keep the highest notes of this scale (especially G^3) really centred.
E♭ Tuba: listen carefully to the intonation of low E and F, compensating with the 4th valve where available.

C MAJOR 2 Octaves

3 E♭ Tuba: take care to centre both pitch and tone of the top three notes of this scale.
F Tuba: special care must be taken to preserve uniformity of tone and intonation across the range. Use the 4th valve where available for C^1.

D♭ MAJOR 1 Octave

4 B♭ Tuba: fingering 2+3 to 1 and back (D♭ to E♭) needs careful co-ordination.
E♭ Tuba: listen carefully to the intonation on low F (F^2), compensating with the 4th valve where available.

D♭ MAJOR A Twelfth

5 F Tuba: low G♭ needs careful tuning; compensate with the 4th valve where available.

D♭ MAJOR 2 Octaves

6 F Tuba: special care must be taken to preserve uniformity of tone and intonation across the range. Low G♭ needs careful tuning; compensate with the 4th valve where available.

7 D MAJOR 1 Octave

7 B♭ Tuba: co-ordinate the fingering from F♯ to G carefully (2+3 to 1+2).
C Tuba: keep the tone as full as possible as you ascend. Listen carefully to the intonation of both Ds, compensating with the 4th valve where available.

8 D MAJOR A Twelfth

8 C Tuba: take care to keep the highest notes of this scale (especially A^3) really centred.
F Tuba: listen carefully to the intonation of low F♯ and G, compensating with the 4th valve where available.

9 D MAJOR 2 Octaves

9 E♭ Tuba: top D is sometimes a little flat. Try 1+2.
F Tuba: take care to centre both pitch and tone of the top three notes of this scale.

10 E♭ MAJOR 1 Octave

10 C Tuba: fingering 2+3 to 1 and back (E♭ to F) needs careful co-ordination.
E♭ Tuba: make sure that 3 goes down simultaneously with 1 on F. Listen carefully to the intonation on F, compensating with the 4th valve where available.
F Tuba: listen carefully to the intonation on low G, compensating with the 4th valve where available.

11 E♭ MAJOR A Twelfth

12 E♭ MAJOR 2 Octaves

12 E♭ Tuba: top D and E♭ are sometimes a little flat. In this case, try 1+2 and 1 respectively.

13 E MAJOR 1 Octave

13 C Tuba: co-ordinate the fingering from G♯ to A carefully (2+3 to 1+2).

14 E MAJOR A Twelfth

15 E MAJOR 2 Octaves (high)

16 E MAJOR 2 Octaves (low)

16 Bb Tuba: take care with the production of the lowest notes of this scale; keep the tone as uniform as possible. Use 2+4 for E^1 if the 4th valve is available.

17 F MAJOR 1 Octave

17 Eb Tuba: keep the tone as full as possible as you ascend. Listen carefully to the intonation of both Fs, compensating with the 4th valve where available.
F Tuba: make sure that 3 goes down simultaneously with 1 on G. Listen carefully to the intonation on G, compensating with the 4th valve where available. Do not let the tone thin out as you ascend.

18 F MAJOR A Twelfth

18 Eb Tuba: take care to keep the highest notes of this scale (especially C^3) really centred.

19 F MAJOR 2 Octaves (high)

20 F MAJOR 2 Octaves (low)

20 Bb Tuba: special care must be taken to preserve uniformity of tone and intonation across the range. Where available, use the 4th valve for F^1.

21 F# MAJOR 1 Octave

21 Eb Tuba: fingering 2+3 to 1 and back (F# to G#) needs careful co-ordination.

22 F# MAJOR A Twelfth (high)

23 F# MAJOR A Twelfth (low)

23 Bb Tuba: low B needs careful tuning; compensate with the 4th valve where available.

24 F# MAJOR 2 Octaves

24 B♭ Tuba: special care must be taken to preserve uniformity of tone and intonation across the range.
C Tuba: take care with the production of the lowest notes in this scale; keep the tone as uniform as possible. Use 2+4 for F#¹ if the 4th valve is available.

25 G MAJOR 1 Octave

25 E♭ Tuba: co-ordinate the fingering from B to C carefully (2+3 to 1+2).
F Tuba: keep the tone as full as possible as you ascend. Listen carefully to the intonation of both Gs, compensating with the 4th valve where available.

26 G MAJOR A Twelfth (high)

26 F Tuba: take care to keep the highest notes of this scale (especially D³) really centred.

27 G MAJOR A Twelfth (low)

27 B♭ Tuba: listen carefully to the intonation of B¹ and C¹, compensating with the 4th valve where available.

28 G MAJOR 2 Octaves

28 B♭ Tuba: take care to centre both pitch and tone of the top three notes of this scale.
C Tuba: special care must be taken to preserve uniformity of tone and intonation across the range. Where available, use the 4th valve for G¹.

29 A♭ MAJOR 1 Octave (high)

29 F Tuba: fingering 2+3 to 1 and back (A♭ to B♭) needs careful co-ordination.

30 A♭ MAJOR 1 Octave (low)

30 B♭ Tuba: listen carefully to the intonation on C¹, compensating with the 4th valve where available.

31 A♭ MAJOR A Twelfth (high)

32 A♭ MAJOR A Twelfth (low)

32 C Tuba: low D♭ needs careful tuning; compensate with the 4th valve where available.

33 A♭ MAJOR 2 Octaves

33 C Tuba: special care must be taken to preserve uniformity of tone and intonation across the range.

34 A MAJOR 1 Octave

34 F Tuba: co-ordinate the fingering from C♯ to D carefully (2+3 to 1+2).

35 A MAJOR A Twelfth (high)

36 A MAJOR A Twelfth (low)

36 C Tuba: listen carefully to the intonation of C♯^{1} and D^1, compensating with the 4th valve where available.

37 A MAJOR 2 Octaves

37 C Tuba: take care to centre both pitch and tone of the top three notes of this scale.
E♭ Tuba: take care with the production of the lowest notes in this scale; keep the tone as uniform as possible. Use 2+4 for A^1 if the 4th valve is available.

38 B♭ MAJOR 1 Octave (high)

39 B♭ MAJOR 1 Octave (low)

39 B♭ Tuba: make sure that 3 goes down simultaneously with 1 on C. Listen carefully to the intonation on C, compensating with the 4th valve where available. Do not let the tone thin out as you ascend.
C Tuba: listen carefully to the intonation on D, compensating with the 4th valve where available.

40 B♭ MAJOR A Twelfth (high)

41 Bb MAJOR A Twelfth (low)

42 Bb MAJOR 2 Octaves

42 Eb Tuba: special care must be taken to preserve uniformity of tone and intonation across the range. Where available, use the 4th valve for Bb¹.

43 B MAJOR A Twelfth

43 Eb Tuba: low E needs careful tuning; compensate with the 4th valve where available.

44 B MAJOR 2 Octaves

44 Eb Tuba: special care must be taken to preserve uniformity of tone and intonation across the range.
F Tuba: take care with the production of the lowest notes in this scale; keep the tone as uniform as possible. Use 2+4 for B¹ if the 4th valve is available.

Minor Scales

45 C MINOR melodic 1 Octave

45 and **46 Bb Tuba**: keep the tone as full as possible as you ascend. Listen carefully to the intonation of both Cs, compensating with the 4th valve where available.
C Tuba: fingering 1+3 to 2+3 (D to Eb) will need careful co-ordination.
Eb Tuba: take care with the production of the lowest notes of these scales. Keep the tone as uniform and as focused as possible.

46 C MINOR harmonic 1 Octave

46 Eb Tuba: fingering 1 to 2+3 and back (Ab to Bb) needs careful co-ordination.

47 C MINOR melodic A Twelfth

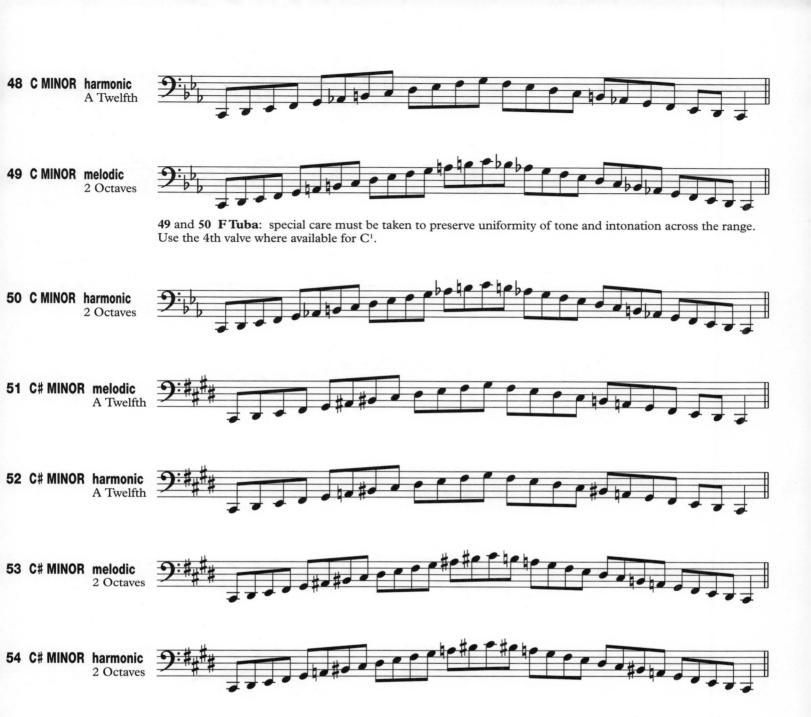

48 C MINOR harmonic A Twelfth

49 C MINOR melodic 2 Octaves

49 and **50 F Tuba**: special care must be taken to preserve uniformity of tone and intonation across the range. Use the 4th valve where available for C¹.

50 C MINOR harmonic 2 Octaves

51 C♯ MINOR melodic A Twelfth

52 C♯ MINOR harmonic A Twelfth

53 C♯ MINOR melodic 2 Octaves

54 C♯ MINOR harmonic 2 Octaves

55 D MINOR melodic 1 Octave

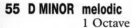

55 and **56 C Tuba**: keep the tone as full as possible as you ascend. Listen carefully to the intonation of both Ds, compensating with the 4th valve where available.
F Tuba: take care with the production of the lowest notes of these scales. Keep the tone as uniform and as focused as possible.

56 D MINOR harmonic 1 Octave

57 D MINOR melodic A Twelfth

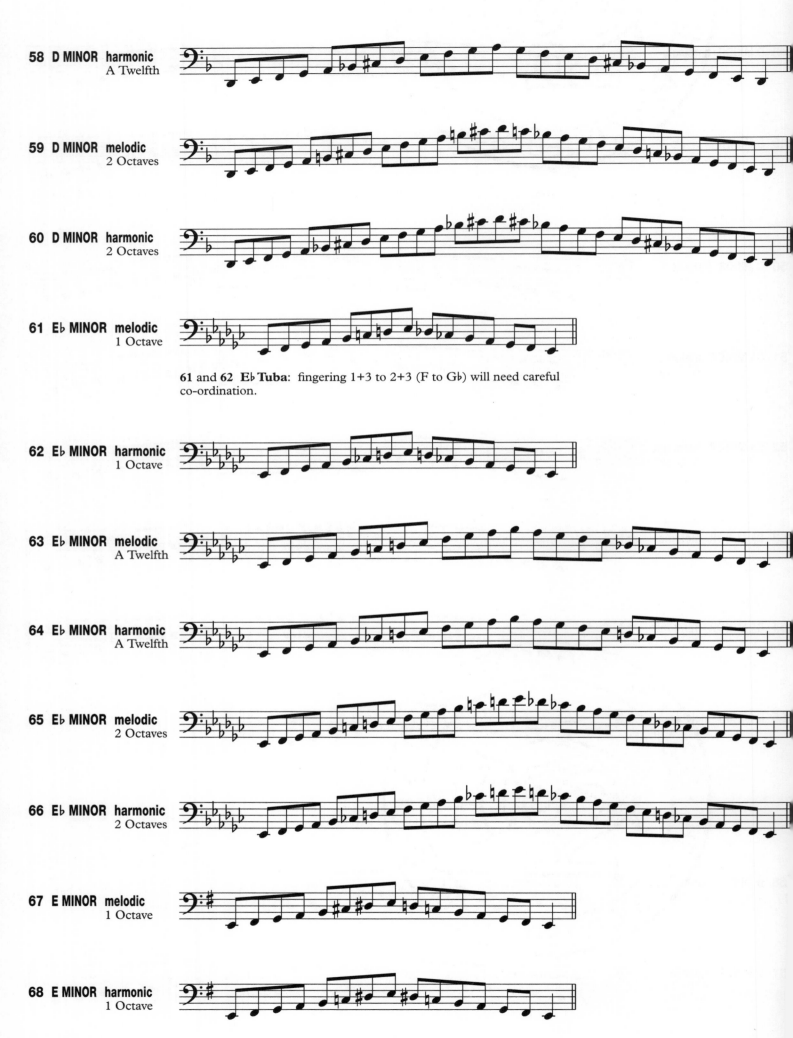

58 D MINOR harmonic
A Twelfth

59 D MINOR melodic
2 Octaves

60 D MINOR harmonic
2 Octaves

61 E♭ MINOR melodic
1 Octave

61 and **62 E♭ Tuba:** fingering 1+3 to 2+3 (F to G♭) will need careful co-ordination.

62 E♭ MINOR harmonic
1 Octave

63 E♭ MINOR melodic
A Twelfth

64 E♭ MINOR harmonic
A Twelfth

65 E♭ MINOR melodic
2 Octaves

66 E♭ MINOR harmonic
2 Octaves

67 E MINOR melodic
1 Octave

68 E MINOR harmonic
1 Octave

75 and **76 E♭ Tuba**: keep the tone as full as possible as you ascend.
Listen carefully to the intonation of both Fs, compensating with the 4th valve where available.
F Tuba: fingering 1+3 to 2+3 (G to A♭) will need careful co-ordination.

79 F MINOR melodic
2 Octaves (high)

80 F MINOR harmonic
2 Octaves (high)

81 F MINOR melodic
2 Octaves (low)

81 and **82 B♭ Tuba**: special care must be taken to preserve uniformity of tone and intonation across the range. Use the 4th valve where available for F^1.

82 F MINOR harmonic
2 Octaves (low)

83 F♯ MINOR melodic
A Twelfth

84 F♯ MINOR harmonic
A Twelfth

85 F♯ MINOR melodic
2 Octaves

86 F♯ MINOR harmonic
2 Octaves

87 G MINOR melodic
1 Octave (high)

87 and **88 F Tuba**: keep the tone as full as possible as you ascend. Listen carefully to the intonation of both Gs, compensating with the 4th valve where available.

88 G MINOR harmonic
1 Octave (high)

89 G MINOR melodic
1 Octave (low)

89 and **90 Bb Tuba:** take care with the production of the lowest notes of these scales. Keep the tone as uniform and as focused as possible.

90 G MINOR harmonic
1 Octave (low)

90 Bb Tuba: fingering 1 to 2+3 and back (Eb to F#) needs careful co-ordination.

91 G MINOR melodic
A Twelfth (high)

92 G MINOR harmonic
A Twelfth (high)

93 G MINOR melodic
A Twelfth (low)

94 G MINOR harmonic
A Twelfth (low)

95 G MINOR melodic
2 Octaves

95 and **96 C Tuba:** special care must be taken to preserve uniformity of tone and intonation across the range. Use the 4th valve where available for G^1.

96 G MINOR harmonic
2 Octaves

97 G# MINOR melodic
1 Octave

98 G# MINOR harmonic
1 Octave

99 G# MINOR melodic
A Twelfth (high)

100 G# MINOR harmonic
A Twelfth (high)

101 G# MINOR melodic
A Twelfth (low)

102 G# MINOR harmonic
A Twelfth (low)

103 G# MINOR melodic
2 Octaves

104 G# MINOR harmonic
2 Octaves

105 A MINOR melodic
1 Octave (high)

106 A MINOR harmonic
1 Octave (high)

107 A MINOR melodic
1 Octave (low)

107 and **108 C Tuba**: take care with the production of the lowest notes of these scales. Keep the sound as uniform and as focused as possible.

108 A MINOR harmonic
1 Octave (low)

108 C Tuba: fingering 1 to 2+3 and back (F to G#) needs careful co-ordination.

109 A MINOR melodic
A Twelfth (high)

110 A MINOR harmonic
A Twelfth (high)

111 A MINOR melodic
A Twelfth (low)

112 A MINOR harmonic
A Twelfth (low)

113 A MINOR melodic
2 Octaves

114 A MINOR harmonic
2 Octaves

115 B♭ MINOR melodic
1 Octave (high)

116 B♭ MINOR harmonic
1 Octave (high)

117 B♭ MINOR melodic
1 Octave (low)

117 and **118 B♭ Tuba**: fingering 1+3 to 2+3 (C to D♭) will need careful co-ordination.

118 B♭ MINOR harmonic
1 Octave (low)

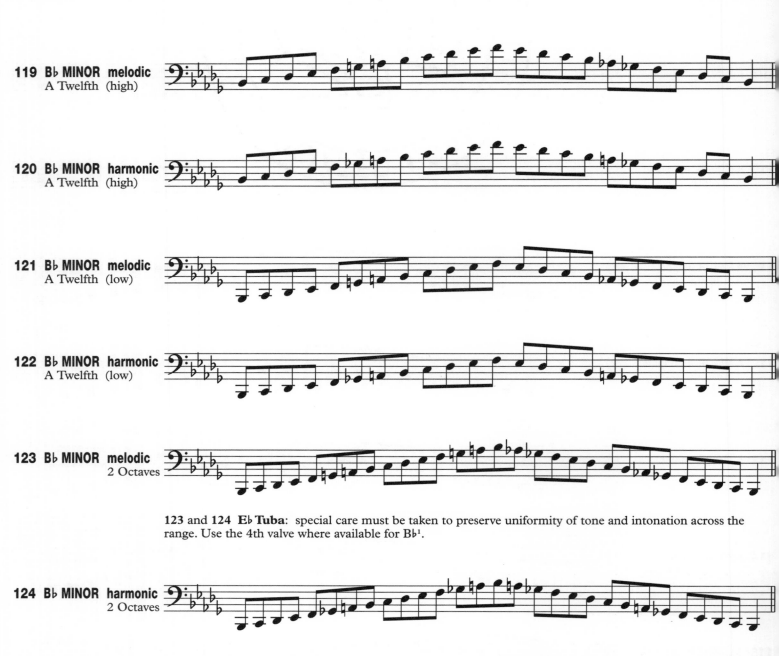

119 B♭ MINOR melodic
A Twelfth (high)

120 B♭ MINOR harmonic
A Twelfth (high)

121 B♭ MINOR melodic
A Twelfth (low)

122 B♭ MINOR harmonic
A Twelfth (low)

123 B♭ MINOR melodic
2 Octaves

123 and **124** **E♭ Tuba**: special care must be taken to preserve uniformity of tone and intonation across the range. Use the 4th valve where available for B♭¹.

124 B♭ MINOR harmonic
2 Octaves

125 B MINOR melodic
A Twelfth

126 B MINOR harmonic
A Twelfth

127 B MINOR melodic
2 Octaves

128 B MINOR harmonic
2 Octaves

Chromatic Scales

NOTE: the breath must be gauged very carefully for 2-octave chromatic scales; aim to preserve uniformity of sound throughout the range, especially when descending. Where available, the use of the 4th valve is essential in the chromatic scale, both to aid intonation and develop fluency in its use.

129 on C 1 Octave

129 C Tuba: listen carefully to the intonation of C^1 and D^1, compensating with the 4th valve where available.

130 on C A Twelfth

131 on C 2 Octaves

132 on C# A Twelfth

135 E♭ Tuba: listen carefully to the intonation of low E and F, compensating with the 4th valve where available.

138 on E 2 Octaves
(high)

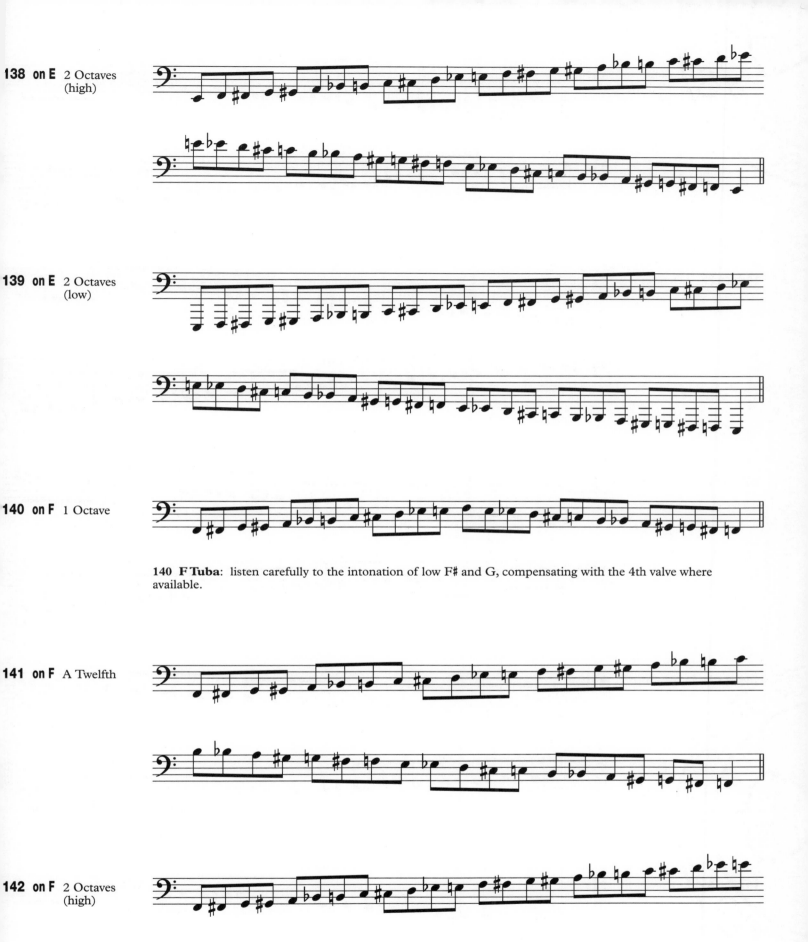

139 on E 2 Octaves
(low)

140 on F 1 Octave

140 F Tuba: listen carefully to the intonation of low F♯ and G, compensating with the 4th valve where available.

141 on F A Twelfth

142 on F 2 Octaves
(high)

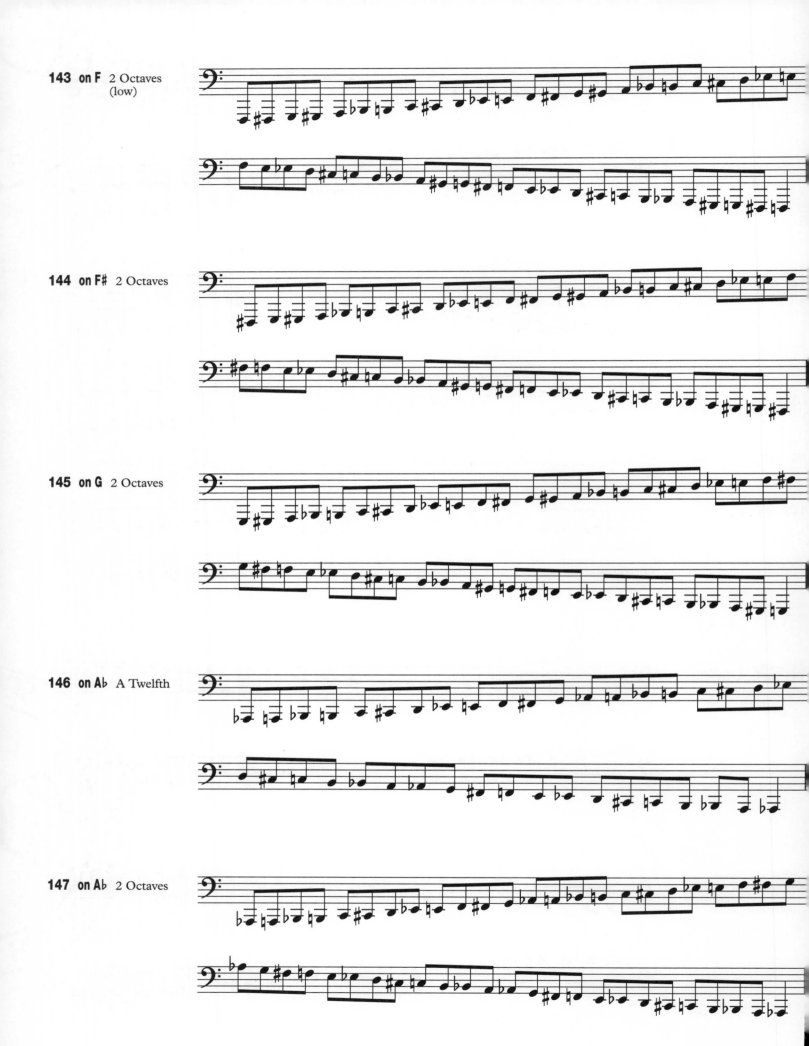

48 on A 2 Octaves

49 on Bb 1 Octave

149 Bb Tuba: listen carefully to the intonation on low B and C, compensating with the 4th valve where available.

50 on Bb A Twelfth

51 on Bb 2 Octaves

52 on B 2 Octaves

Whole-Tone Scales

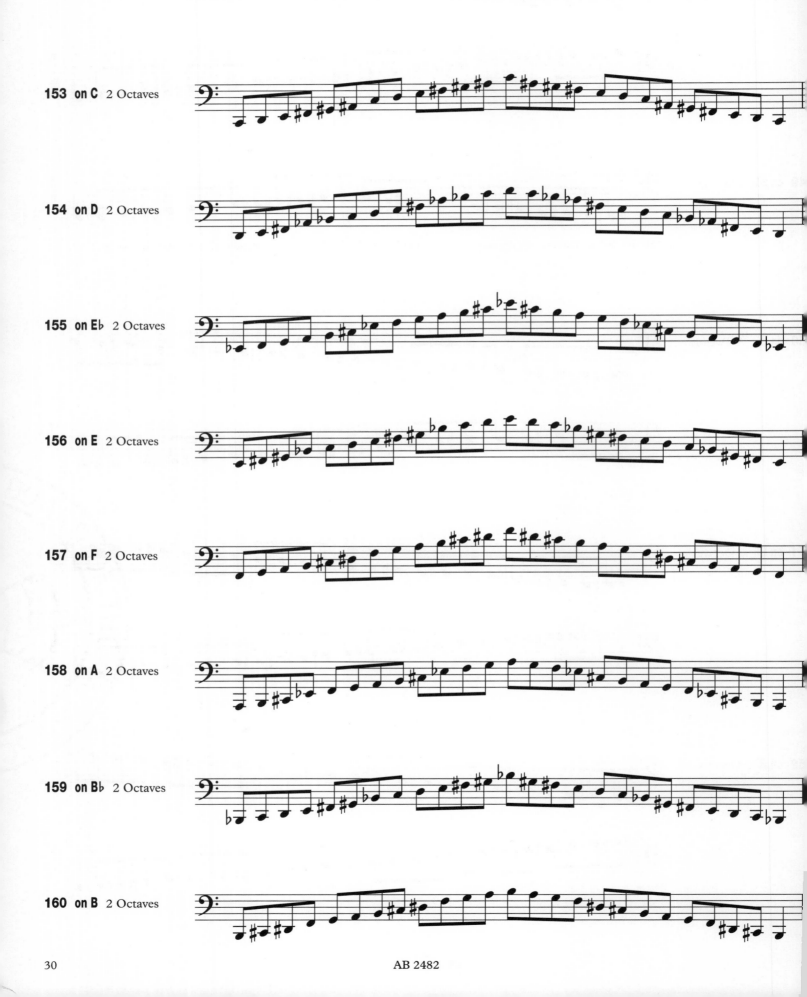

153 on C 2 Octaves

154 on D 2 Octaves

155 on E♭ 2 Octaves

156 on E 2 Octaves

157 on F 2 Octaves

158 on A 2 Octaves

159 on B♭ 2 Octaves

160 on B 2 Octaves

AB 2482

Major Arpeggios

161 C MAJOR 1 Octave

161 B♭ Tuba: finger co-ordination needs care throughout, especially when slurred; using the 4th valve where available will eradicate this problem and improve intonation.
C Tuba: take special care when negotiating G to C and back, especially when slurred.

162 C MAJOR A Twelfth

162 B♭ Tuba: keep a really centred sound on top G.

163 C MAJOR 2 Octaves

163 F Tuba: take care to preserve uniformity of sound throughout the range, especially when descending.

164 D♭ MAJOR 1 Octave

164 E♭ Tuba: listen carefully to the intonation on F, compensating with the 4th valve where available.

165 D♭ MAJOR A Twelfth

165 and **166 E♭ Tuba:** as most of the notes in these arpeggios are played with the 1st valve, lip flexibility must be carefully calculated, especially when slurred.

166 D♭ MAJOR 2 Octaves

167 D MAJOR 1 Octave

167 C Tuba: finger co-ordination needs care throughout, especially when slurred; using the 4th valve where available will eradicate this problem and improve intonation.

168 D MAJOR A Twelfth

169 D MAJOR 2 Octaves

170 Eb MAJOR 1 Octave

170 Eb Tuba: take special care when negotiating Bb to Eb and back, especially when slurred.
F Tuba: listen carefully to the intonation on G, compensating with the 4th valve where available.

171 Eb MAJOR A Twelfth

171 and 172 F Tuba: as most of the notes in these arpeggios are played with the 1st valve, lip flexibility must be carefully calculated, especially when slurred.

172 Eb MAJOR 2 Octaves

173 E MAJOR 1 Octave

174 E MAJOR A Twelfth

175 E MAJOR 2 Octaves (high)

176 E MAJOR 2 Octaves (low)

176 Bb Tuba: take care to preserve uniformity of sound throughout the range, especially when descending.

177 F MAJOR 1 Octave

177 Eb Tuba: finger co-ordination needs care throughout, especially when slurred; using the 4th valve where available will eradicate this problem and improve intonation.
F Tuba: take special care when negotiating C to F and back, especially when slurred.

AB 2482

178 F MAJOR A Twelfth

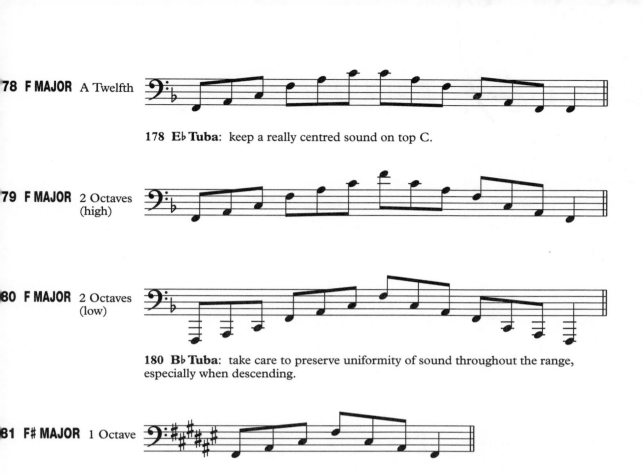

178 E♭ Tuba: keep a really centred sound on top C.

179 F MAJOR 2 Octaves (high)

180 F MAJOR 2 Octaves (low)

180 B♭ Tuba: take care to preserve uniformity of sound throughout the range, especially when descending.

181 F♯ MAJOR 1 Octave

182 F♯ MAJOR A Twelfth (high)

183 F♯ MAJOR A Twelfth (low)

184 F♯ MAJOR 2 Octaves

184 C Tuba: take care to preserve uniformity of sound throughout the range, especially when descending.

185 G MAJOR 1 Octave

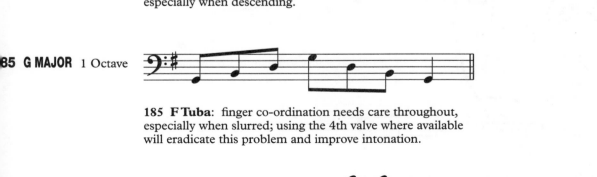

185 F Tuba: finger co-ordination needs care throughout, especially when slurred; using the 4th valve where available will eradicate this problem and improve intonation.

186 G MAJOR A Twelfth (high)

186 F Tuba: keep a really centred sound on top D.

187 G MAJOR A Twelfth (low)

188 G MAJOR 2 Octaves

188 C Tuba: take care to preserve uniformity of sound throughout the range, especially when descending.

189 Ab MAJOR 1 Octave (high)

190 Ab MAJOR 1 Octave (low)

190 Bb Tuba: listen carefully to the intonation on C, compensating with the 4th valve where available.

191 Ab MAJOR A Twelfth (high)

192 Ab MAJOR A Twelfth (low)

192 and 193 Bb Tuba: as most of the notes in these arpeggios are played with the 1st valve, lip flexibility must be carefully calculated, especially when slurred.

193 Ab MAJOR 2 Octaves

194 A MAJOR 1 Octave

195 A MAJOR A Twelfth (high)

196 A MAJOR A Twelfth (low)

197 A MAJOR 2 Octaves

197 E♭ Tuba: take care to preserve uniformity of sound throughout the range, especially when descending.

198 B♭ MAJOR 1 Octave (high)

199 B♭ MAJOR 1 Octave (low)

199 B♭ Tuba: take care when negotiating F to B♭ and back, especially when slurred.
C Tuba: listen carefully to the intonation on D, compensating with the 4th valve where available.

200 B♭ MAJOR A Twelfth (high)

201 B♭ MAJOR A Twelfth (low)

201 and **202 C Tuba:** as most of the notes in these arpeggios are played with the 1st valve, lip flexibility must be carefully calculated, especially when slurred.

202 B♭ MAJOR 2 Octaves

202 E♭ Tuba: take care to preserve uniformity of sound across the range, especially when descending.

203 B MAJOR A Twelfth

204 B MAJOR 2 Octaves

204 F Tuba: take care to preserve uniformity of sound throughout the range, especially when descending.

Minor Arpeggios

205 C MINOR 1 Octave

205 B♭ Tuba: listen carefully to the intonation on low C, compensating with the 4th valve where available.
E♭ Tuba: keep the tone on low C as steady as possible. Take special care when negotiating G to C and back, especially when slurred.

206 C MINOR A Twelfth

206 and 207 E♭ Tuba: lip flexibility needs care here, especially when slurred.

207 C MINOR 2 Octaves

207 F Tuba: take care to preserve uniformity of sound throughout the range, especially when descending.

208 C♯ MINOR A Twelfth

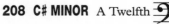

209 C♯ MINOR 2 Octaves

209 E♭ Tuba: take care when negotiating top G♯ to C♯ and back, especially when slurred.

210 D MINOR 1 Octave

210 C Tuba: listen carefully to the intonation on low D, compensating with the 4th valve where available.
F Tuba: keep the tone on low D as steady as possible. Take special care when negotiating A to D and back, especially when slurred.

211 D MINOR A Twelfth

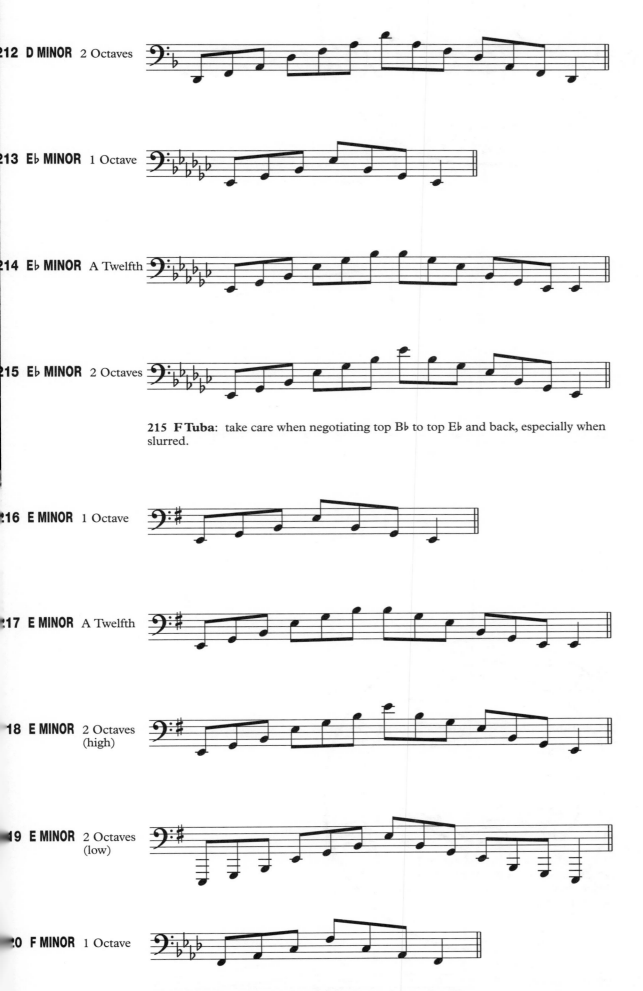

212 D MINOR 2 Octaves

213 E♭ MINOR 1 Octave

214 E♭ MINOR A Twelfth

215 E♭ MINOR 2 Octaves

215 F Tuba: take care when negotiating top B♭ to top E♭ and back, especially when slurred.

216 E MINOR 1 Octave

217 E MINOR A Twelfth

218 E MINOR 2 Octaves (high)

219 E MINOR 2 Octaves (low)

220 F MINOR 1 Octave

220 E♭ Tuba: listen carefully to the intonation on low F, compensating with the 4th valve where available.

221 F MINOR A Twelfth

222 F MINOR 2 Octaves (high)

223 F MINOR 2 Octaves (low)

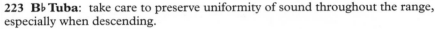

223 B♭ Tuba: take care to preserve uniformity of sound throughout the range, especially when descending.

224 F♯ MINOR A Twelfth

225 F♯ MINOR 2 Octaves

226 G MINOR 1 Octave (high)

226 F Tuba: listen carefully to the intonation on low G, compensating with the 4th valve where available.

227 G MINOR 1 Octave (low)

227 B♭ Tuba: keep the tone on low G as steady as possible. Take special care when negotiating D to G and back, especially when slurred.

228 G MINOR A Twelfth (high)

229 G MINOR A Twelfth (low)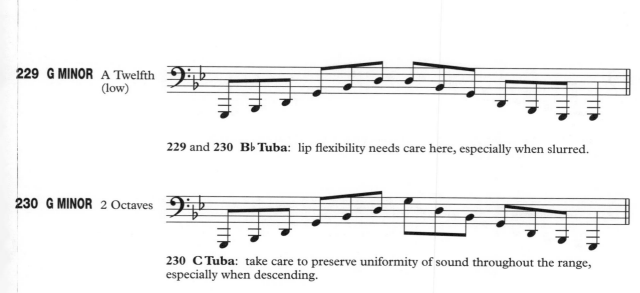

229 and **230 B♭ Tuba**: lip flexibility needs care here, especially when slurred.

230 G MINOR 2 Octaves

230 C Tuba: take care to preserve uniformity of sound throughout the range, especially when descending.

231 G♯ MINOR 1 Octave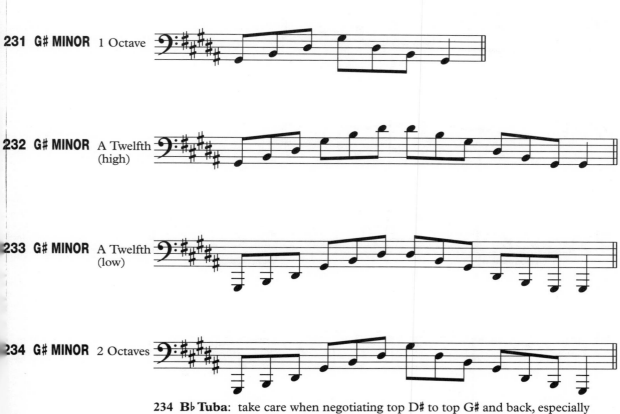

232 G♯ MINOR A Twelfth (high)

233 G♯ MINOR A Twelfth (low)

234 G♯ MINOR 2 Octaves

234 B♭ Tuba: take care when negotiating top D♯ to top G♯ and back, especially when slurred.

235 A MINOR 1 Octave (high)

236 A MINOR 1 Octave (low)

236 C Tuba: keep the tone on low A as steady as possible. Take special care when negotiating E to A and back, especially when slurred.

237 A MINOR A Twelfth (high)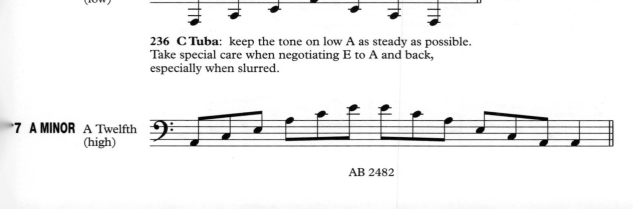

238 A MINOR A Twelfth (low)

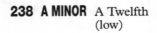

238 and **239 C Tuba**: lip flexibility needs care here, especially when slurred.

239 A MINOR 2 Octaves

240 Bb MINOR 1 Octave (high)

241 Bb MINOR 1 Octave (low)

242 Bb MINOR A Twelfth (high)

243 Bb MINOR A Twelfth (low)

244 Bb MINOR 2 Octaves

244 C Tuba: take care when negotiating top F to top Bb and back, especially when slurred.
Eb Tuba: take care to preserve uniformity of sound throughout the range, especially when descending.

245 B MINOR A Twelfth

246 B MINOR 2 Octaves

Dominant Sevenths

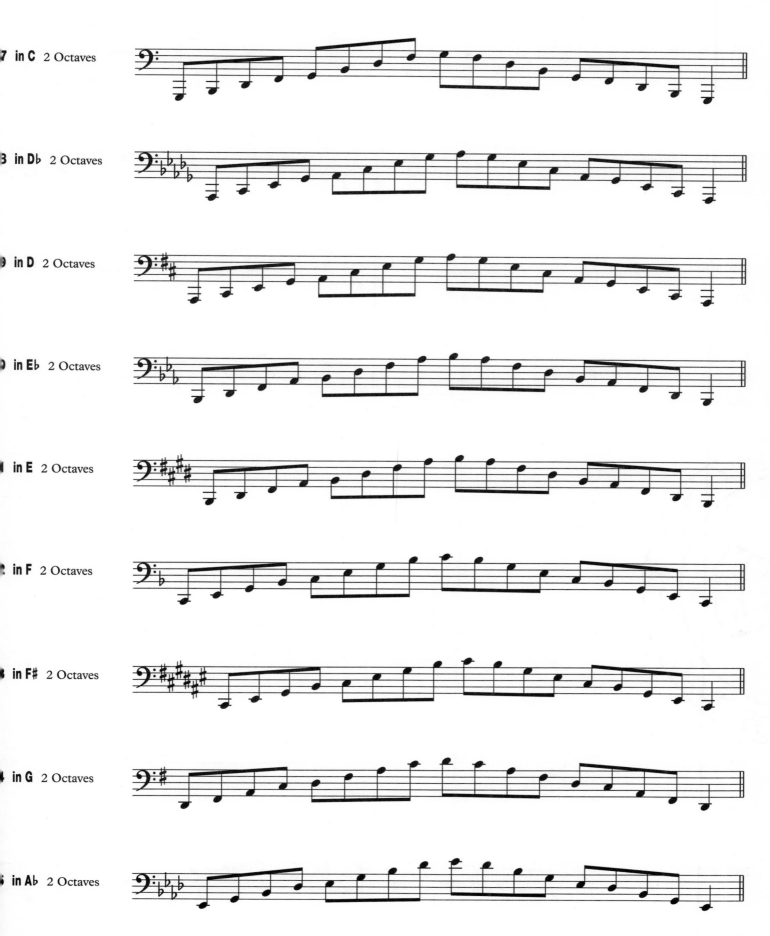

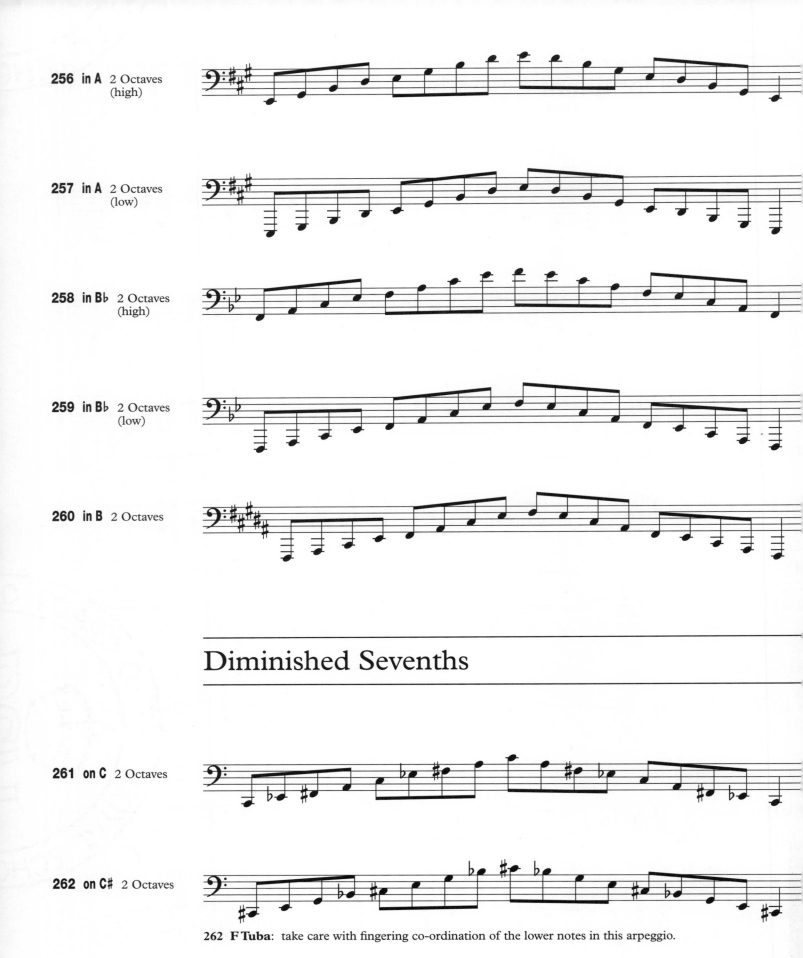

256 in A 2 Octaves (high)

257 in A 2 Octaves (low)

258 in B♭ 2 Octaves (high)

259 in B♭ 2 Octaves (low)

260 in B 2 Octaves

Diminished Sevenths

261 on C 2 Octaves

262 on C# 2 Octaves

262 F Tuba: take care with fingering co-ordination of the lower notes in this arpeggio.

263 on D 2 Octaves

266 Bb Tuba: take care with fingering co-ordination of the lower notes in this arpeggio.

268 C Tuba: take care with fingering co-ordination of the lower notes in this arpeggio.

271 Eb Tuba: take care with fingering co-ordination of the lower notes in this arpeggio.

ic and text origination by
es Music Engraving Ltd, East Sussex
red by Caligraving Ltd, Thetford, Norfolk

5

4 on Eb 2 Octaves

5 on F 2 Octaves

6 on F# 2 Octaves

7 on G 2 Octaves

8 on Ab 2 Octaves

9 on A 2 Octaves

0 on Bb 2 Octaves

1 on B 2 Octaves